Look and Find™

DISNEY PRINCESS

Hidden
Trinkets & Treasures

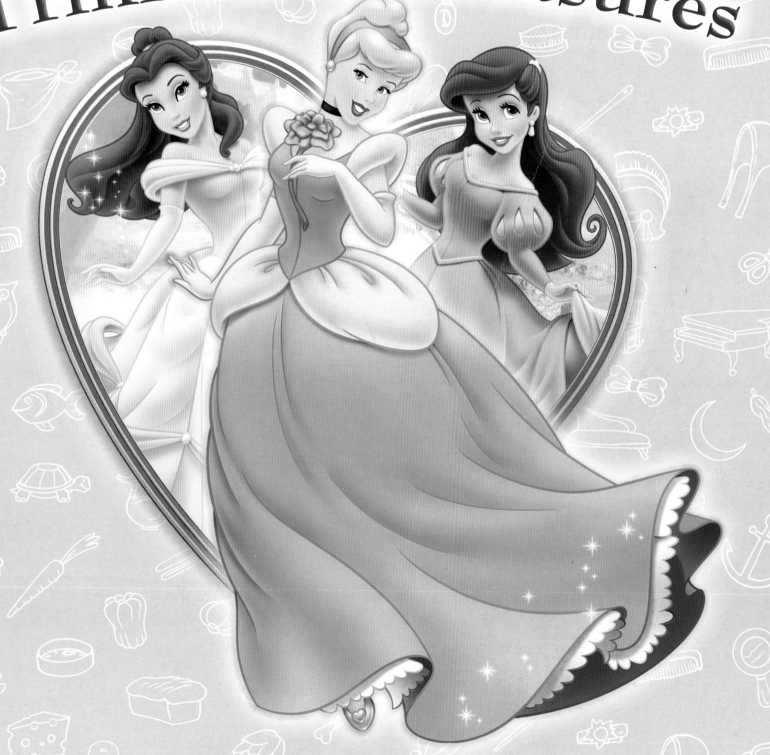

pi kids® publications international, ltd.

Snow White loved spending time with the Seven Dwarfs and her forest friends. Can you find these hidden critters in the cottage?

Mama Odie helped Tiana get back to New Orleans and find true love. Can you find these hidden items Tiana will need if she opens up her restaurant?

Ariel wanted to be human
forever. All she had to do
was get Prince Eric to kiss her.
See if you can find these nautical
items hidden around the lagoon.

During Jasmine's magic carpet ride with Prince Ali, she realized he was Aladdin — the boy from the marketplace. It didn't matter to Jasmine that he wasn't a prince. Can you find these hidden trinkets and treasures of Agrabah?

Thanks to the Fairy
Godmother, Cinderella's
dream came true!
She went to the royal ball
and met Prince Charming.
Can you find these things
from Cinderella's old home?

Rapunzel finally got to watch the lanterns on her birthday. Can you find all the hidden hats, helmets, and headwear she saw on her journey?

Over time, Belle learned that the Beast wasn't just gruff and grumbly — he had a kind and tender side. Just as Belle found the Beast's true nature, can you find these hidden objects?

True Love's Kiss broke the curse! Aurora and Prince Phillip lived happily ever after. Can you find these hidden reminders of Aurora's former home in the forest?

More Find'ems!

Want even more Look and Find challenges? Here are more find'ems for each scene.

Can you find these other hidden friends in the Seven Dwarfs' cottage?

Hop back to Mama Odie's and see if you can find these other hidden foods items.

Swim back to the blue lagoon and look for these nautical novelties.

Go back and see which of these hidden treasures you can find with Jasmine and Aladdin.

Try not to lose a glass slipper looking for these hidden reminders of Cinderella's chores.

Find these hidden items that Rapunzel could wear on her head or use to style her hair.

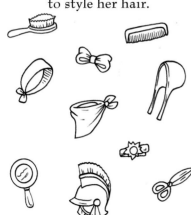

Can you find these furnishings hidden outside the Beast's castle?

Are you able to find these items hidden around Aurora's fairy-tale ending?

Answer Keys

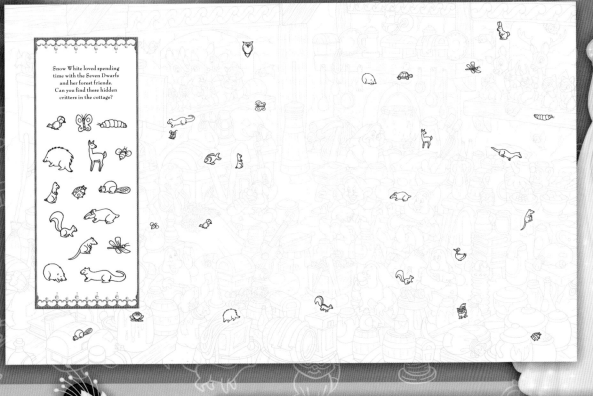

Snow White loved spending time with the Seven Dwarfs and her forest friends. Can you find these hidden critters in the cottage?

Mama Odie helped Tiana get back to New Orleans and find true love. Can you find these hidden items Tiana will need if she opens up her restaurant?

Ariel wanted to be human forever. All she had to do was get Prince Eric to kiss her. See if you can find these nautical items hidden around the lagoon.

During Jasmine's magic carpet ride with Prince Ali, she realized he was Aladdin — the boy from the marketplace. It didn't matter to Jasmine that he wasn't a prince. Can you find these hidden trinkets and treasures of Agrabah?

Thanks to the Fairy Godmother, Cinderella's dream came true! She went to the royal ball and met Prince Charming. Can you find these things from Cinderella's old home?